684040963941

KU-375-011

Bigfoots
at the Beach

Maverick
Early Readers

'Bigfoots at the Beach'
An original concept by Rebecca Colby
© Rebecca Colby 2023

Illustrated by Tamás Mayer

Published by MAVERICK ARTS PUBLISHING LTD
Studio 11, City Business Centre, 6 Brighton Road,
Horsham, West Sussex, RH13 5BB
© Maverick Arts Publishing Limited February 2023
+44 (0)1403 256941

A CIP catalogue record for this book is available at the British Library.

ISBN 978-1-84886-930-1

www.maverickbooks.co.uk

This book is rated as: Yellow Band (Guided Reading)
It follows the requirements for Phase 3 phonics.
Most words are decodable, and any non-decodable words are familiar,
supported by the context and/or represented in the artwork.

Bigfoots
at the Beach

By Rebecca Colby

Illustrated by
Tamás Mayer

Bab and Bud are bigfoots.

Bab sits near the fan.

"I feel hot."

Bud sits near the door.

"I feel hotter."

Bud digs in the sand.

"This is high!"

Bab plays in the sand.

"This is higher!"

Bab splashes Bud. "You are wet!"

Bud splashes Bab. "You are wetter!"

Bud picks up a shell. "This is big!"

Bab picks up a shell. "This is bigger!"

24

Bab licks her ice cream. "I feel cool."

Bud licks his ice cream. "I feel cooler."

Quiz

1. Where do the bigfoots go?
a) To the pool
b) To the beach
c) To the lake

2. What does Bud do in the sand?
a) Dig in it
b) Jump on it
c) Play in it

3. Where do the bigfoots go for a dip?
a) The sea
b) A pool
c) A bath

4. What is in the shell?
a) A pebble
b) A crab
c) A fish

5. What do the bigfoots eat?
a) Hot dogs
b) Chips
c) Ice cream

Turn over for answers

Book Bands for Guided Reading

The Institute of Education book banding system is a scale of colours that reflects the various levels of reading difficulty. The bands are assigned by taking into account the content, the language style, the layout and phonics. Word, phrase and sentence level work is also taken into consideration.

Maverick Early Readers are a bright, attractive range of books covering the pink to white bands. All of these books have been book banded for guided reading to the industry standard and edited by a leading educational consultant.

To view the whole Maverick Readers scheme, visit our website at www.maverickearlyreaders.com

Or scan the QR code above to view our scheme instantly!

Pink
Red
Yellow
Blue
Green
Orange
Turquoise
Purple
Gold
White

Quiz Answers: 1b, 2a, 3a, 4b, 5c